CONTENTS

KU-043-424

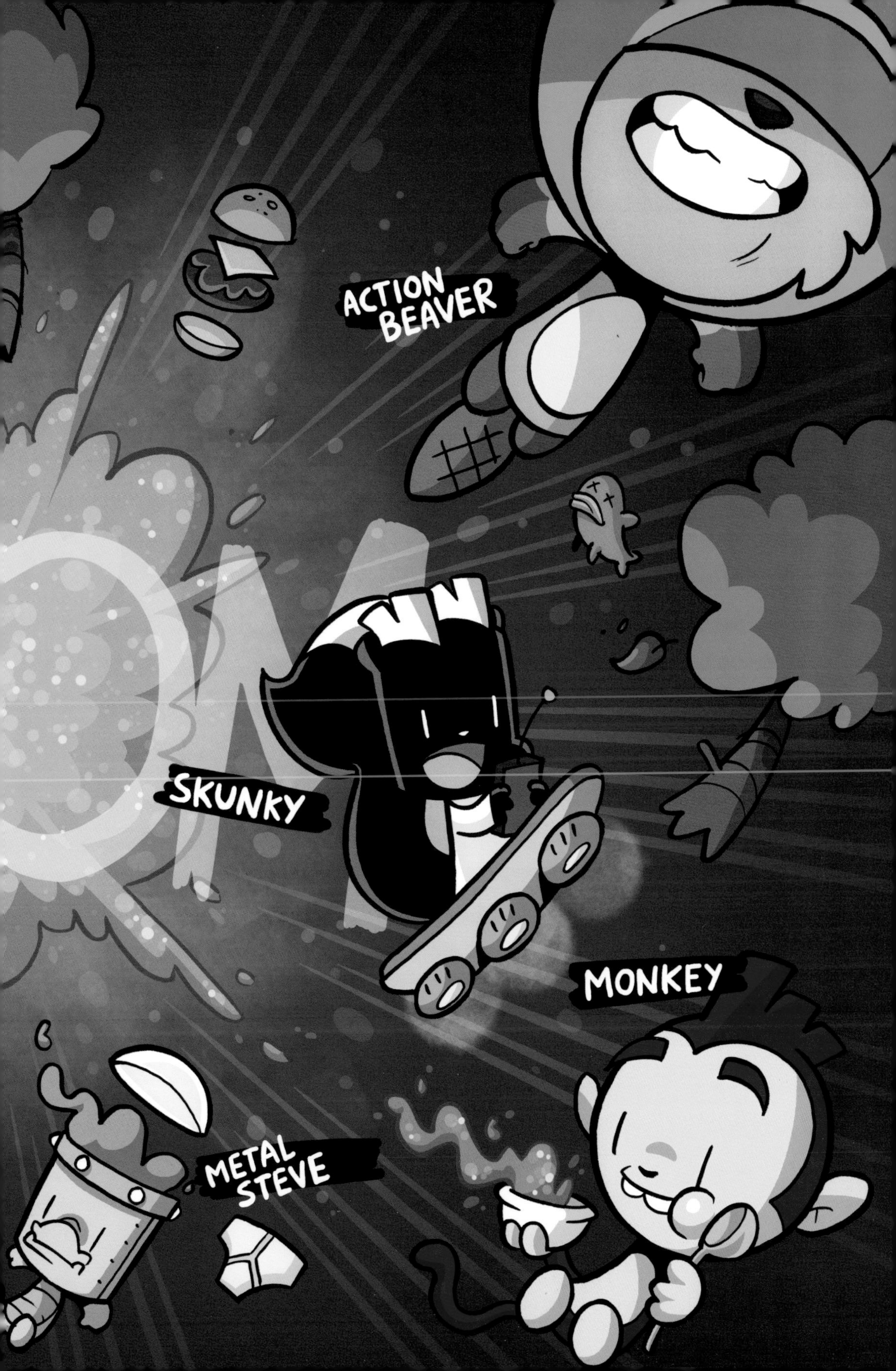
ACTION BEAVER
SKUNKY
MONKEY
METAL STEVE

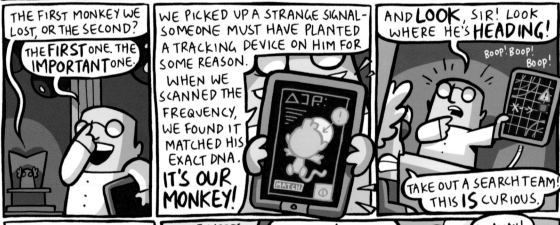

RRGH! I TRIED TO BE AN EVIL TYRANT, BUT NO ONE WOULD LET ME! SO I TRIED TO BE A GOOD GUY, AND I NEARLY DIIIIIIIED OF THE BOREDOM!

SO LET ME IN YOUR GANG NOW.

GOT HIM! JUST BEFORE HE HAD THE CHANCE TO GO INSIDE!

THUNK!

RRFF!

?

PSCHH!

WE'VE BEEN LOOKING FOR YOU FOR A LONGGGG TIME, LITTLE MONKEY.

AND NOW YOU'RE OURS.

THPTHBTHH!

HUMAN BEINGS! THIS FAR INTO THE WOODS?

AND MONKEY'S IMPORTANT TO THEM?

MONKEY'S NOT IMPORTANT TO ANYONE.

BOOP!!

I CAN'T LET THEM TAKE HIM! RELEASE... THE CLUCKEN!!

BUCKK-AWW!

UHH, STEVE? WHAT'S THAT?

WHAT'S WHAT?

BUCKK-RK-AWWWW!!

AIIIEE!

WE SHOULD HAVE STAYED AWAY FROM THIS PLACE!

SKUNKY! YOU... YOU SAVED ME!

YEAH, ALL RIGHT. DON'T GO ON ABOUT IT.

IF THOSE HUMANS WANT YOU SO MUCH, YOU MUST BE SPECIAL FOR SOME REASON. SO IT MAKES TACTICAL SENSE TO KEEP YOU WITH ME UNTIL WE DISCOVER WHY.

I'M SPECIAL?

YES.

MONKEY, YOU ARE NOW IN MY LEAGUE OF DOOM! AND NOT ONLY THAT, YOU ARE A VITAL MEMBER!

BRILL! WHAT CAN I DO FIRST? PLAY WITH YOUR HORRIFIC INVENTIONS? DESTROY EVERYTHING IN SIGHT?

ACTION BEAVER BLOCKED THE TOILET AGAIN. GET SCRUBBING.

AW, POO.

YES.

JAMIE

7

...WE TAKE THEM TO SKUNKY!

SKUNKY! WE HAVE A PRESENT FOR YOU!

POOO-EEE! GET WHATEVER THAT IS AWAY FROM MY EVIL HEADQUARTERS!

IT'S POOP!

POOP. AND WE NEED YOU TO THINK UP A WAY WE CAN DISPOSE OF IT!

WHYYY WOULD I HELP YOU?

BECAUSE OTHERWISE, THE WOODS WILL FILL UP WITH POOP!

BLEURGH, FAIR POINT.

POOP!

AS YOU CAN SEE FROM MY EXTENSIVE PLANS, THE BEST WAY TO DISPOSE OF VAST QUANTITIES OF POOP...

...IS TO FIRE IT AT THE MOON!!

POOP. MOON!

Result = No more poop!

THE POOP CANNON!

POOP!

UMM...I'M NOT SURE THAT'S THE BEST WAY.

BEHOLD! THE APPLICATION OF SCIENCE TO POOP!

TWANG!

PTOO!

POOOOP!

MISTER SKUNKY, HOW FAR AWAY IS THE MOON?

OH, IT CAN'T BE THAT FAR. I CAN SEE IT FROM HERE!

WEENIE, A LOT OF SCIENCE IS ABOUT CROSSING YOUR FINGERS AND HOPING...

IT'S COMING BACK DOWN!

I DIDN'T FIRE IT FAR ENOUGH!!

EEE!

GIBBER GIBBER!

POOP!

EUGH!!

LATER...

POOOOP!

I KEEP SCRUBBING BUT I CAN STILL SMELL IT!

IT'S STILL IN MY FUR!

THIS IS OUR FIFTH BATH! OUR FIFTH BATH!

JAMIE

A-HEM! EXCUSE ME, WOULD YOU MIND NOT HUGGING MY **ULTIMATE WEAPON**?!

HEE HEE! WHAT ARE YOU? A **CAT**? A LITTLE BLACK-AND-WHITE **KITTY CAT**?

NO! I AM THE MOST **EVIL** SUPER-GENIUS IN THE **WORLD**!

HEE HEE! WHAT CUTE FRIENDS YOU HAD HERE, STEVE.

NOT CUTE! A **SUPER-GENIUS**! **SUPER-GENIUS**!

AND A **SKUNK** TOO! **LOOK**!

FRRP! FRRP!

STINK! GUFF!

A WHIFFY SKUNK! A STINKY, GROSS...

SHE'S GONE, SKUNKY.

BUT... BUT THAT LITTLE GIRL STOLE MY ULTIMATE WEAPON!

WELL, HE SEEMED QUITE HAPPY TO GO WITH HER.

HE DID.

MAYBE HE'S FOUND A **REAL** HOME NOW, SKUNKY.

* SNIFF *

BACK IN SKUNKY'S HQ...

MAYBE BUNNY'S RIGHT. MAYBE METAL STEVE **DOES** DESERVE A BETTER LIFE. MAYBE I SHOULD JUST ACCEPT HE'S GONE.

OR, MAYBE I SHOULD USE HIS REMOTE CONTROL TO **RUIN** THEIR NEW FRIENDSHIP!

BIT GRUMPY
ANGRY
DESTRUCTO
APOCALYPSE

UMM...

BOOP!

BZZT!

BOOMF!!!

WAHOO!

BZZT! FRIENDSHIP ANNIHILATED. RESUME DESTRUCTION.

STEVE! YOU CAME BACK!

MEANWHILE, IN TOWN...

WE NEED TO TALK ABOUT THE KIND OF FRIENDS YOU KEEP, ELOUISE.

WAHHH!

11

"WAHEY-ELL"

A CALM SUMMER MORNING IN THE WOODS - THE BIRDS ARE SINGING...

...A GIANT WHALE IS CRASHING THROUGH THE TREES...

...WAIT, **WHAT?**

CRASH! ★ CRASH!

HAR HAR! THANKS FOR LETTING ME TEST-DRIVE YOUR **WAHEY-ELL**, SKUNKY!

CONSIDER IT A TRIAL, TO SEE WHETHER YOU DESERVE TO BE IN THE **LEAGUE OF EVIL!**

SMASH! CRASH!

THERE! THERE'S BUNNY'S HOUSE! STEER THAT WAY, AND **FLATTEN** IT!

AYE AYE!

LOOK AT ME, BUNNY! I'M FINALLY IN SKUNKY'S GANG!

RUMMMBLE!

AND WE'RE GOING TO SMASH YOUR HOUSE UP!

AUGUST

"THE ORDER OF THE WOODS"

ZZNCKK!

WAS I DRIBBLING?

AWAKE, SLEEPING BUNNY! WE ARE THE ORDER OF THE WOODS, A SECRET AND MYSTERIOUS CULT, AND YOU ARE OUR PRISONER!

WHERE AM I? WHO ARE YOU?

SIGH...

WE ARE THE ORDER OF THE WOODS, A SECR...

START FROM THE BEGINNING.

AWAKE, SLEEPING BUNNY! WE ARE THE...

YEAH, ALL RIGHT, I GOT THAT BIT. WHY AM I NOT IN MY HOUSE?

WE SNEAKED YOU OUT, TO BRING YOU FAR BELOW GROUND.

RARR!

...TO SEE IF YOU CAN ESCAPE THE LABYRINTH!

IF YOU DO, YOU MAY STAY IN THE WOODS. IF YOU DON'T, WELL, YOU'LL PROBABLY HAVE BEEN FLATTENED OR SOMETHING.

BUT... WHY?

WHY... WHAT?

WHY DO I HAVE TO PLAY THIS SILLY GAME? WHO PUT YOU IN CHARGE?

BECAUSE WE ARE THE ORDER OF THE WOODS!

AND WE HAVE AN ELECTRIC PROD!

BZZAP!

YARGH! OKAY, I'M GOING!

14

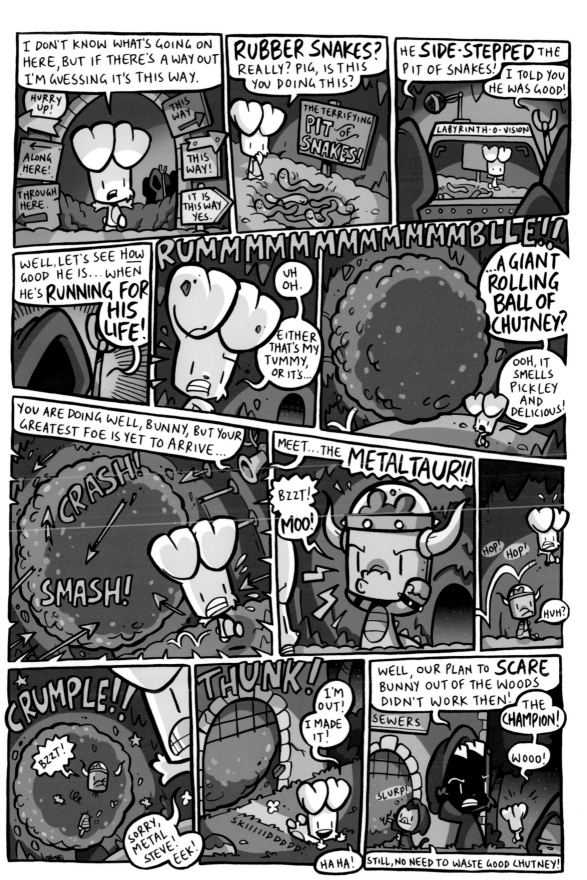

"BENEATH THE WAVES"

HERE WE ARE, MONKEY! SAT INSIDE MY NEWEST VEHICLE...

...THE W1000 AQUEOUS SUBMERSIBLE!

OR "WASSSUB", FOR SHORT.

WE'RE FULLY EQUIPPED FOR EVERY SITUATION.

LIFEJACKETS, OXYGEN MASKS, SANDWICH DISPENSER, FREE WI-FI...

THAT'S ALL GREAT, BUT...

LIFE RAFT

THE RIVER DOESN'T GO ANY DEEPER THAN THIS.

HA! SILLY, UNAMBITIOUS MONKEY! WHAT WE NEED IS **UNDERNEATH** THE RIVER!

WASSSUB

I'VE BEEN SURVEYING THESE WOODS WITH INFA-RED SATELLITE LASERS, AND I'VE DISCOVERED A HUGE UNDERGROUND **LAKE** DIRECTLY BENEATH US!

ALL WE HAVE TO DO...

...IS DIG OUR WAY DOWN TO IT!

BOOP!

ACTIVATE GARDEN SPADES

DIG! DIG! DIG! DIG! DIG! DIG! DIG! DIG! DIG! DIG! SPLISH! DIG! DIG! DIG! DIG! DIG! DIG! SPLASH!

20

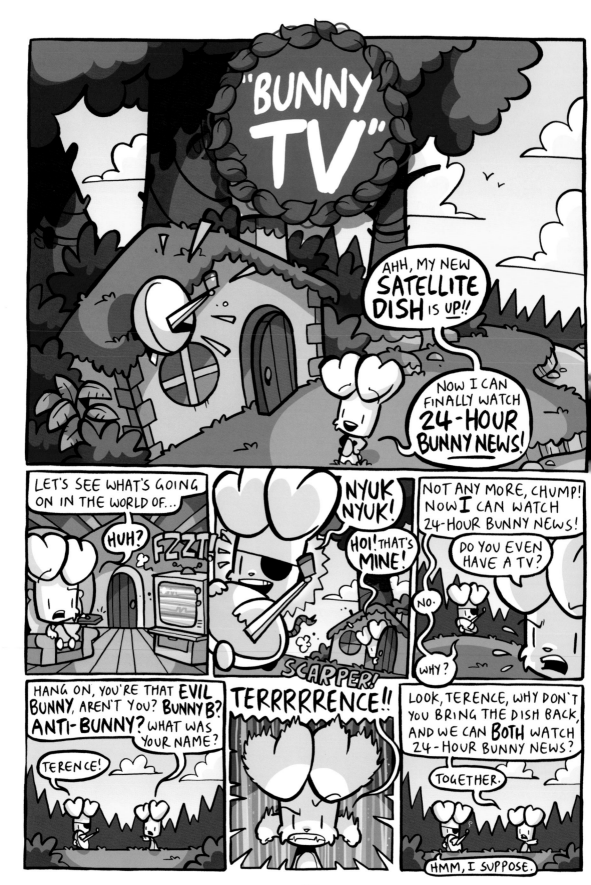

27

'MONKEY WITH A FLAME-THROWER'

HAR HAR! HARHARHAR!

FWOOM!!

HAR!!

BUNNY, ARE YOU IN?

I'VE MADE A BIT OF A BOO-BOO.

KNOCK! KNOCK!

BUNNY WENT ON HOLIBOBS! I AM HOUSE-SITTING!

RRGH! WHAT BAD TIMING!

MONKEY GOT INTO MY **CANNON BARREL** AND STOLE THE **FIRE CANNON**!

I NEEDED BUNNY'S HELP TO STOP HIM BURNING UP THE **WOODS**!

CANNON BARREL

MONKEY KEEP OUT!

I CAN HELP! MAYBE THERE'S A CANNON IN HERE WE CAN FIGHT HIM WITH!

HMM, WELL I GUESS THE OPPOSITE OF A FIRE CANNON WOULD BE...

...THE ICE CANNON!

BUT I DON'T THINK YOU SHOULD...

I CAN DO THIS! I CAN DO THIS!

BWARPP!

ERK!

I DID THIS!

28

"AN IMPORTANT MESSAGE"

PIG AND WEENIE WANDERING AROUND... HAVING ADVENTURES... HAVING LAUGHS...

KEEP

FINDING NEW THINGS... SEEING SOME THINGS... STRUGGLING TO MAKE SONGS RHYME...

GRUHHHHHH!!

AIII-EEE!

LE FOX! YOU'RE BACK!

WHERE'VE YOU BEEN ALL THIS TIME? WE SORT OF MISSED YOU!

I HAVE BEEN DEEP, DEEP UNDERCOVER, CONCEALED WITHIN SKUNKY'S LABORATORY!

I HAVE EXPLORED THE SECRET ROOMS, OBSERVED THEIR DIABOLICAL PLANS, AND HIDDEN IN THE TOILET.

PARP!

I HAVE UNCOVERED SKUNKY'S TRUE INTENTIONS, AND WATCHED HIM DO RIDICULOUS THINGS TO A TORTOISE.

PLIP!

I HAVE DONE ALL THIS, SO...HEY! WHERE ARE YOU GOING?

OH, SORRY!

WE THOUGHT YOU'D FINISHED.

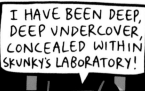

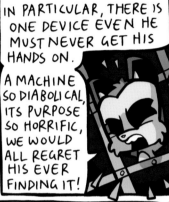

"MIXEY-MATOSIS"

IN THE DEPTHS OF SKUNKY'S EVIL LABORATORY...

BWOOP! BWOOP! BWOOP!

METAL STEVE! WHAT HAPPENED HERE?

BZZT! SOMEONE SET OFF THE ANIMAL DNA SPLICE DEVICE.

NOT SURE WHO, THOUGH.

CHOMP! CHOMP!

?

HUNDREDS OF ANIMALS, REDUCED TO A MOLECULAR LEVEL AND THEN COMBINED TOGETHER!

WHO KNOWS WHAT BEASTS WILL CRAWL OUT!

MEANWHILE, ABOVE GROUND...

PIG! I'VE INVENTED A GAME. YOU STAND THERE, AND THEN WAVE AT ME!

OKAY! HEE HEE! WHAT FUN!

AND THEN I WAVE BACK!

YAYY!

WAVE! WAVE!

WAVEY! WAVE!

CHICKEN FISH!

AIIIEE! IS THIS PART OF THE GAME?

SCREE-EEEE-EAM!

NO.

CLUCK CLUCK BLOOP!

BUNNY! LOOK OUT! IT'S COMING TOWARDS YOU!

SIGH. SOMETHING USUALLY IS.

"CAMPING"

AHH! THE GREAT OUTDOORS!

INTO THE WILDERNESS!

CAN WE SIT DOWN? MY POTATOES ARE VERY HEAVY.

PIG, WHY **HAVE** YOU BROUGHT A BIG SACK OF POTATOES?

YOU CAN NEVER HAVE TOO MANY POTATOES.

BUT WE'RE ONLY OUT FOR THE DAY!

NEVER. TOO. MANY.

WELL, YOU'RE SLOWING US DOWN. IT'S DIFFICULT ENOUGH JUST WORKING OUT WHERE WE ARE!

MAP

I THINK IT'S THIS WAY?

ONWARDS!

WOODS

YUKON

MORE WOODS

MY POTATOES DON'T FEEL SO HEAVY. I MUST BE GETTING STRONGER!

YAY PIG!

WELL DONE, PIG.

RIGHT! THIS LOOKS LIKE A GOOD PLACE TO SET UP CAMP.

WEENIE, YOU WERE IN CHARGE OF THE TENT.

"THE MONO-CHROMATRON"

HANG ON, DID I WAKE UP IN THE OLDEN DAYS?

BUNNY, WE'RE GREY!

WE GOT OLD!

HMM, THAT'S ONE POSSIBILITY. THE OTHER, MORE LIKELY POSSIBILITY, IS THAT SKUNKY HAS DONE SOMETHING TO SUCK ALL OF THE COLOUR OUT OF THE WORLD!

WOOD·O·VISION

"SKUNKY DID IT!" MEH MEH MEH! SKUNKY SKUNKY SKUNKY! IT'S ALWAYS ME THEY BLAME, ISN'T IT.

VWUP! VWUP! VWUP!

I THOUGHT YOU DID DO IT?

WELL, YES, I DID. I JUST RESENT BEING THE FIRST ONE THEY THINK OF.

BUT YOU WANTED THEM TO KNOW HOW BRILLIANT YOU ARE!

OH YES. I DO.

THAT'S WHY YOU MADE ME WEAR THIS HAT.

NOT THE BRILLIANT ONE

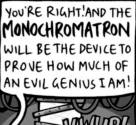

YOU'RE RIGHT! AND THE MONOCHROMATRON WILL BE THE DEVICE TO PROVE HOW MUCH OF AN EVIL GENIUS I AM!

VWUP!

EVERY BEAUTIFUL COLOUR STOLEN FROM NATURE AND CONCEALED INSIDE...

"THE LAST BROADCAST"

HERE, METAL STEVE!

THIS WAY!

FOLLOW THE TRAIL OF NUTS AND BOLTS!

MMM! CHOMP! CHOMP!

CLANG! CHOMP!

FOUND YOU!

BUNNY, YOU'RE TERRIBLE AT HIDE N' SEEK!

WHAT? I WASN'T PLAYING HIDE N' SEEK!

YOU WEREN'T? WHY NOT?

I'M TOO BUSY! DO YOU REMEMBER THOSE STRANGE METAL PLATES IN THE GROUND WHICH, WHEN METAL STEVE STOOD ON THEM, TRANSFORMED HIM INTO A MEGA ROBOT?!

NO.

NO.

WELL, I WANT HIM TO STAND ON ONE OF THEM AGAIN!

BECAUSE I FOUND HIS INSTRUCTION MANUAL, AND I THINK I CAN OVERRIDE THE ACTIVATION!

PROJECT: METAL STEVE

AND THEN USE HIM TO FIRE GREAT BIG MISSILES AT SKUNKY'S LABORATORY!

WHEE!

WHERE DID YOU GET ALL THESE BITS OF METAL FROM?

MY CAR!

RANGER

DUNNO. FOUND THEM. AHA! WE'RE HERE! EVERYONE GET READY FOR METAL STEVE'S AMAZING TRANSFORMATION!

HMM.

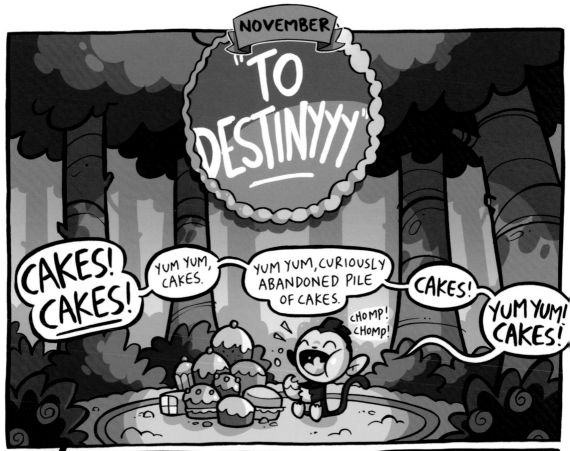

"TO DESTINYYY"

"FIND THE MONKEY"

SO!! THIS IS WHAT WE KNOW SO FAR...

SKUNKY'S EVIL LAIR IS **ACTUALLY** THE OLD MEANIECORP BUILDING...

...MEANIECORP CREATED TERRIFYING EXPERIMENTS...

...INCLUDING **METAL STEVE**...

...BUT HAD TO EVACUATE WHEN THEY UNLEASHED A MYSTERIOUS ANCIENT MONSTER CALLED THE **MOSHOGGOTH!**

THIS MEANS SKUNKY IS SITTING ON TOP OF A **GREAT BIG MONSTER**, AND HE DOESN'T EVEN KNOW IT!

YES HE DOES!

SKUNKY! YOU WERE HIDING UNDER A NAPKIN ALL THIS TIME? I THOUGHT ONE OF YOU MIGHT NOTICE, BUT...

...NOPE.

FINE! I **DIDN'T** INVENT METAL STEVE LIKE I SAID I DID. WHO CARES? IT WAS **ME** WHO MADE IT SO HE COULD TRANSFORM INTO A **MOTORBIKE!**

BRMM!

WHO'S COOL? IS IT ME? IT'S ME! BRUMM!

THE MONSTER, SKUNKY!

THE **MOSHOGGOTH!**

THPTHBTHH! THAT'S JUST A MYTH. THERE'S NO SUCH THING AS MONSTERS!

APART FROM ALL THE MONSTERS I MAKE.

OBVIOUSLY.

ANYWAY, I CAME ROUND TO ASK IF YOU'VE SEEN MONKEY? HE'S GONE MISSING, AND MY TOILETS WON'T CLEAN THEMSELVES.

WELL, THEY DO, BUT DON'T TELL HIM THAT.

UMM... NO. I HAVEN'T SEEN HIM.

IT'S STARTING TO SNOW OUTSIDE! HE MIGHT BE **COLD**!

OUT OF MY WAY! MONKEY'S WEARING A **TRACKER**, SO I CAN SEE WHERE HE IS AT ANY TIME!

I CAN JUST...

BEEP! BOOP!

...OH, THAT'S WEIRD. IT CAN'T FIND HIM **ANYWHERE**!

BEWOOOO.

MONKEY TRACKER

THE ONLY WAY THAT WOULD HAPPEN IS IF...

...HE DOESN'T EVEN **EXIST** ANY MORE!!

OUT OF <u>MY</u> WAY! WE HAVE TO FIND MONKEY!

GIBBER!

THIS WAS HIS FAVOURITE PILE OF MUD TO SIT IN...

PUFF! WHEEZE!

DIG! DIG!

BOG

THIS WAS HIS FAVOURITE TREE TO DROP JELLY ON BUNNY FROM.

SO **THAT'S** WHO IT WAS!

LOOK, WEENIE, SLOW DOWN. LET'S NOT LOOK <u>TOO</u> HARD FOR MONK—

I'VE <u>DONE</u> IT!

I'VE BUILT US A **NEW** MONKEY!

TAA-DAA!

THIS MONKEY IS MADE FROM A STRAW-FILLED SACK. ALSO, HE DOESN'T FART OR ANSWER BACK!

GASP! HE'S PERFECT!

HAR HAR! ARE YOU SERIOUS? I COULD CONSTRUCT A **FAR** BETTER MONKEY, MERELY BY USING HIS DNA...

MONKEY THINKS YOU'RE A RUDE SHOW-OFF!!

CLO-NK!

YARGH!

RETREAT! **RETREAT!** THIS MONKEY'S **FAR** MORE DANGEROUS THAN THE REAL ONE!

BOO HOO HOO!

JAMIE

45

"SABO-TAGE"

A FEW WEEKS AGO...

YAWWWNN!

WHAT A LOVELY DAY OF EVIL WE'VE HAD!

GNAW! GNAW!

TIME FOR BED, I THINK.

BUT BEFORE I DO...

I MUST PLACE A SAUCER OF MILK, AND THE SECRET SCHEMATICS FOR **THE MOST DEVASTATING WEAPON THE WORLD HAS EVER KNOWN**, IN FRONT OF THIS VENT.

AS USUAL.

≥CLICK!≤

NIGHTY NIGHT!

ZAT DEVIOUS SKUNK!

HE KNOWS I'M HIDING IN ZE AIR DUCTS!

HE'S TRYING TO LURE ME OUT!

WELL ZIS TIME, IT HAS WORKED.

LET US JUST HAVE A QUICK LOOK...

CRE-EEE-EAK!

AH. LE FOX. SO KIND OF YOU TO JOIN US.

CLICK!

ZUT!!

46

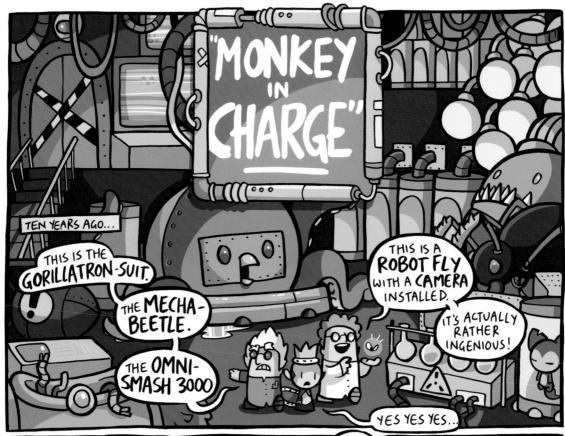

"MONKEY IN CHARGE"

TEN YEARS AGO...

THIS IS THE **GORILLATRON-SUIT**.

THE **MECHA-BEETLE**.

THE **OMNI-SMASH 3000**

THIS IS A **ROBOT FLY** WITH A **CAMERA** INSTALLED.

IT'S ACTUALLY RATHER INGENIOUS!

YES YES YES...

"...BUT WHEN CAN I SMASH STUFF?"

MONKEY, AS THE NEW CHIEF SCIENCE OFFICER- ...SIGH...AS THE NEW **KING** OF MEANIECORP, YOU CAN USE ANY OF OUR WEAPONS AT ANY TIME.

KING.

BRILLIANT! LET'S GO!

HOWEVER, IT IS IMPORTANT THAT YOU UNDERSTAND HOW THEY **WORK**, FIRST.

...MMY

HERE AT MEANIECORP, WE STUDY **LIFE**. NATURE'S GLORIOUS BOUNTY OF CREATURES! AND WE USE WHAT WE LEARN FROM THE ANIMAL KINGDOM TO CREATE INCREDIBLE CREATIONS OF DESTRUCTION.

SIR! HE'S IN THE INCREDIBLE CREATION OF DESTRUCTION!

BRUM! BRUM!

I'M IN CHARGE! TOOT TOOT!

ARGH!

I'M REALLY NOT SURE WHY **FUTURE-ME** SENT YOU BACK HERE TO TAKE CHARGE.

I'M GOING TO TAKE OVER THE WORLD!

"THE MONSTROUS BELOW"

BOOMF!

So much for a subtle entrance.

?

Knock knock, Mister Skunky!

STAND BACK! OR ELSE I WILL UNLEASH THE MOST **DEVASTATING WEAPON IN THE WORLD!**

YOU CAN'T FOOL US. YOU'VE ALREADY USED IT!

I HAVE?

YOU **MUST** HAVE. STRANGE THINGS ARE HAPPENING OUT IN ZE WOODS!

PIG AND WEENIE DON'T EVEN REMEMBER WHATSISNAME ANY MORE.

WHO?

SEE?!

LOOK AT MY **PAW**, SKUNKY. IT HAS BEEN SLOWLY DISAPPEARING...

JUST LIKE PIG'S **NOSE**... AND BUNNY'S **EAR**...

MY WHAT... AUGH!

SKUNKY, YOUR WEAPON. WHAT DOES IT ACTUALLY **DO?**

IT'S A **REALITY DISCOMBOBULATOR** IT BENDS SPACE AND TIME, WARPING DIMENSIONS!

SO THIS **IS** YOUR FAULT!

IT CAN'T BE! I HAVEN'T WORKED OUT HOW TO TURN IT **ON.**

HAVE YOU NOT NOTICED ANY WEIRD THINGS HAPPENING?

WELL, MONKEY DISAPPEARED. THAT WAS WEIRD. AND EVER SINCE THEN, THERE'S BEEN THIS STRANGE RUMBLING UNDERNEATH THE GROUND.

RUMMMMBLE!!

THERE IT IS AGAIN! I THINK THE TOILETS ARE BACKING UP!

SHRIEK!

SKUNKY, IT MIGHT BE CONNECTED TO ALL THIS! WE HAVE TO FIND OUT WHAT'S DOWN THERE!

OKAY! OKAY!

I WILL COME WITH YOU. I CAN...

NO, LE FOX. TAKE PIG AND WEENIE FAR AWAY FROM HERE!

BOO HOO!

BUT... I AM ZE PROTECTOR OF ZE WOODS!

IT IS MY DUTY TO FIX ZIS...

ONE OF US HAS WET OURSELF!

WELL, ALL THE PLUMBING LEADS DOWN HERE..

I'VE NEVER DARED GO THIS FAR, THOUGH.

TOO CREEPY!

RUMMMMBLE!

NYAHHH!

GOOD IDEA! YOU GO FIRST!

I CAN'T SEE ANYTHING! IT'S TOO DARK!

BUNNY?

BUNNY? IS THAT YOU?

GAAAASP!

MONKEY! HOW LONG HAVE YOU BEEN DOWN HERE?

OH, YEARS. EVER SINCE THEY SHUT IT AWAY.

SHUT WHAT AWAY?

I CAN'T EVEN REMEMBER. I USED TO RUN THIS WHOLE LABORATORY, Y'KNOW.

THEN I GOT GREEDY. SET IT LOOSE.

THEY TOLD ME TO HOLD THIS DOOR WHILE THEY ESCAPED.

MONKEY...

SET WHAT LOOSE?

53

footer:

58

"REMEMBERING FRIENDS"

IT'S STILL IN ONE PIECE! MY HIDDEN CORNER OF MEANIECORP! MY LAB! MY BEAUTIFUL, BEAUTIFUL LAB!

AW, SHAME.

MY ANNIHILATOR! MY SMASHYOVERDRIVEATRON! I'M SO SORRY I LEFT YOU.

MWAH! MWAH!

KISS KISS!

EXCELLENT NEWS! LET US RESUME OUR HAVOC WREAKING IMMEDIATELY, SKUNKY!

WHAT? WHY SHOULD I TAKE ORDERS FROM YOU?

UM, NEED I REMIND YOU, SKUNKY, THAT MONKEY ONCE RULED MEANIECORP LABS AND VERY NEARLY DESTROYED REALITY ITSELF JUST BY EXISTING!!

IT COULD BE ARGUED THAT, PURELY BY ACCIDENT, HE'S THE MOST DANGEROUS MONKEY ALIVE!

UGH!

I DID WHAT?

YOU MIGHT BE WISER TO KEEP HIM CLOSE, THAN ANNOY HIM.

FINE. FINE! WHAT SHALL WE INVENT FIRST THEN, MONKEY?

A GIANT MECHANICAL SAUSAGE!!

MAYBE I'LL LEAVE YOU TWO TO IT.

ABOVE GROUND...

OH! HEY, IS THAT THE SKUNK'S SECRET LAIR?

YEAH. LOOKS LIKE HE'S BACK IN ACTION.

THESE WOODS MIGHT GET A LITTLE...CRAZY AGAIN.

BRILLIANT! I LOVE CRAZY!

YOU **DO?** WELL, WOULD YOU WANT TO HANG AROUND? WE COULD SURE DO WITH THE HELP, NOW LE FOX IS...GONE.

I'D LOVE TO! MY NAME IS **AI!**

HEH.

IT'S SHORT FOR **AYE-AYE!**

WHAT'S AN AYE-AYE?

I-I AM!

SHAKEY-SHAKE!

I'M SORRY ABOUT YOUR FOX FRIEND, BY THE WAY. THE WAY HE TOOK DOWN THAT MOSHOGGOTH THOUGH - AMAZING!

YEAH. HE WAS A REAL HERO.

THEN WE MUST **REMEMBER** HIM. LIKE, **PROPERLY!**

WHAT DO YOU MEAN?

BUILD SOMETHING TO HONOUR HIM!

WHAT A GREAT IDEA! AND I KNOW JUST WHO WOULD WANT TO BUILD IT!

QUITE SOME TIME LATER...

WE'VE DONE IT, BUNNY! MOST OF LE FOX'S HEAD IS HEDGE, BUT WE HID SOME CAKES IN IT SO BIRDS WOULD SIT ON HIM.

I'M SURE LE FOX WOULD LOVE IT!

NO, HE WOULDN'T. HE'D BE VERY VERY GRUMPY ABOUT IT.

AND THAT'S EXACTLY HOW I THINK HE'D WANT TO BE REMEMBERED.

CLANG! CLANG! CLANG!

ONWARDS, INTO YEAR 4 OF BUNNY VS MONKEY!

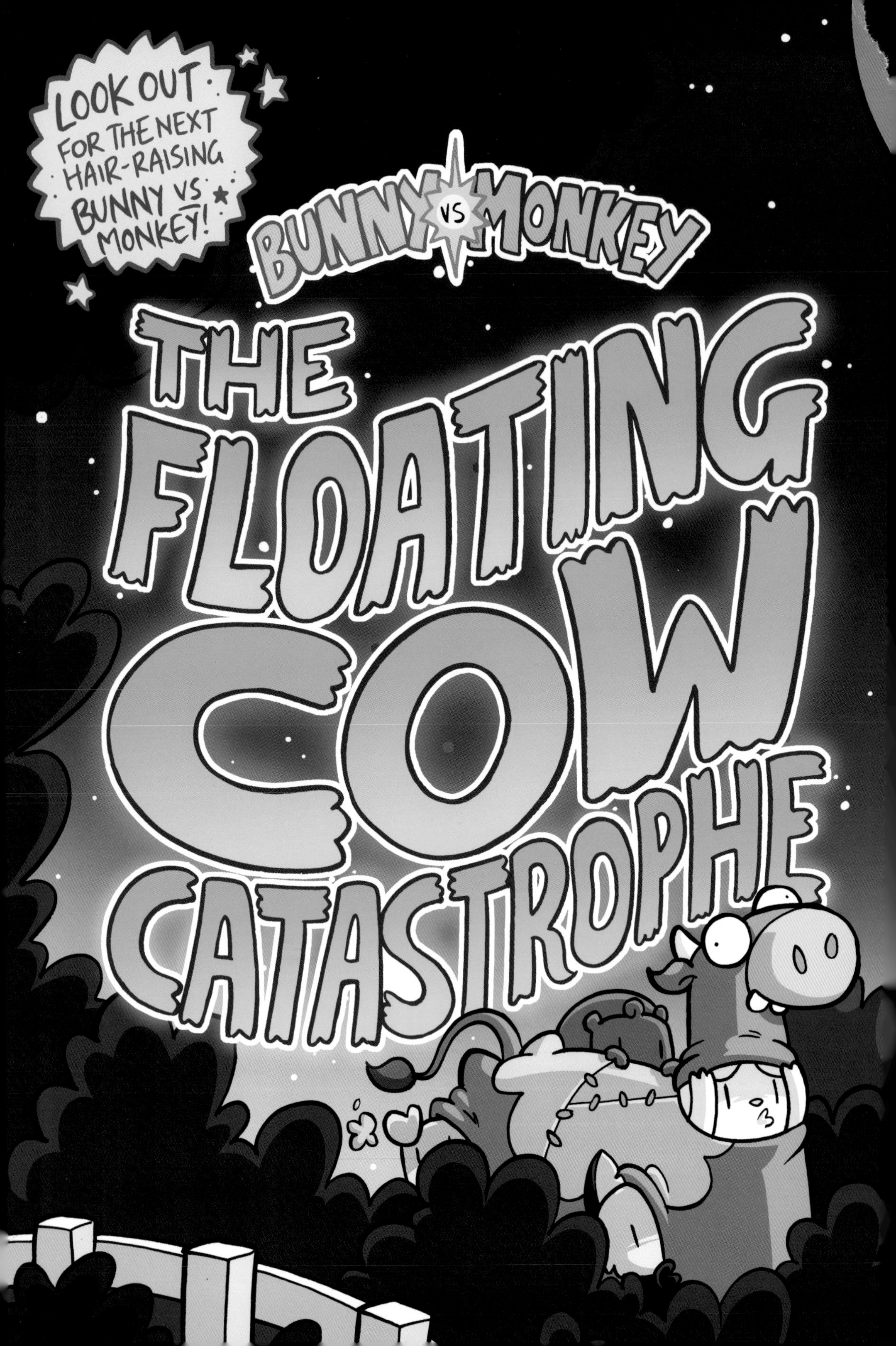
LOOK OUT FOR THE NEXT HAIR-RAISING BUNNY VS MONKEY!
BUNNY VS MONKEY
THE FLOATING COW CATASTROPHE